Winter Fun Book

To Emma,
With love from
Mrs Hogh

July '92

periscope
- page 40

This edition first published 1988 by
The Hamlyn Publishing Group Limited
Michelin House
81 Fulham Road
London
SW3 6RB
England
By arrangement with Ellsyd Press
an imprint of David Ell Press Pty Ltd
137-139 Regent Street, Chippendale 2008
Australia.

Copyright © 1988 Text: Anne Ingram & Peggy O'Donnell
           © 1988 Illustrations: Mark David

ISBN 0 600 560 015

Printed in Hong Kong through Colorcraft Ltd

Winter Fun Book

Anne Ingram and Peggy O'Donnell

Illustrations by

Mark David

HAMLYN

Contents

I suggest you go straight to page 24.

Winter is Fun

Winter *is* fun, even if the days are shorter and the nights longer, it doesn't mean there are fewer hours — there are still 24! And it has been proved, by scientists, that regardless of whether it's winter or summer, we will still be awake for about 16 hours and asleep for about 8 hours.

So plan your winter months — don't waste them. It's the ideal time to catch-up on all those indoor activities you put aside during the summer — like sorting out your stamp collection, or catching up on your reading.

We have filled this book with dozens of suggestions of things to do, inside and out, during the winter months. These are our ideas, you'll have lots more, and at the end we have given you an A-Z of surviving winter! But to begin. Here are a few pieces of useless information you can dazzle your friends with — they're all about winter, of course!

Winter trivia

Acute Nasopharyngitis is the scientific name for the common cold.

In 1887, thousands of sheep were killed by a violent ice storm in Texas, U.S.A.

Arctic beetles and Alaskan flies have a built-in antifreeze, they survive in temperatures of −60°C. Although they freeze, ice crystals form outside the cells, which are undamaged. Glycerol and other substances in their body fluids work like the antifreeze in a car.

Even in temperate latitudes, the wind helps decide how cold we will feel. This is called the "chill factor". As a general rule you can subtract 1°C from the air temperature for every 3 km of wind speed (10°F for every 1 mph). So if it was 15°C and there was a strong wind of 48 km/h, the temperature will feel as cold as about −1°C (30°F).

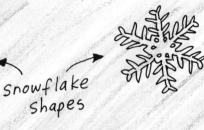

snowflake shapes

The Weddell seal of the Antarctic and the ringed seal of the Arctic both survive on and under the ice all year round. To hunt beneath the frozen seas, these seals will bore a series of breathing holes through the ice, which can be as much as 3 m (10 ft) thick. They return to these holes to breathe between dives.

If the temperature in the clouds is below freezing, then snow is formed from the millions of tiny ice crystals. However, it will not fall to the ground as snow unless the temperature is freezing all the way down (otherwise it will fall as sleet or rain).

Examine a snowflake under a microscope and you will find they really make very beautiful patterns, and they will always have six sides.

Sometimes, as the winter begins, you will see plagues of small animals, such as mice, swarming across the fields searching for the last seeds and berries of summer.

Hail is caused by frozen rain which is carried upwards in a cloud and then falls through a layer of freezing air.

Fog happens when the ground temperature drops rapidly, on a clear night, and condensation occurs. Fog usually settles in the hollows.

Frost is when the ground temperature is below freezing and the dew turns to ice and frost.

The snow flakes fall too fast to see them.

Try looking at the top of this page.

Winter Fun Game

Forgot to clean bird table. Miss a turn

Saw first birds migrating. Have another turn

Made a bird-seed feeder. Move ahead 2 spaces

Put out fresh water for birds. Have another turn

Raked up the leaves. Have another turn

Left window open. Miss a turn

Left rake in garden. Throw 4 to move

Potted spring bulbs. Move ahead 1 space

Sorted out stamp collection. Move ahead 2 spaces

Put away toys. Have another turn

Left playroom in a mess. Throw 6 to move

Spilt the potting mix. Miss 2 turns

Left muddy wellies in kitchen. Miss a turn

Cleaned the family's shoes. Have another turn

Start

Filled wellies with snow. Go back 2 spaces

Took dog for long walk. Move ahead 3 spaces

How to Play

Two or more players.

You need a dice and a counter for each player.

The person who gets highest number goes first.
Then take turns to throw the dice and move the
number of spaces. You must follow the
instructions written on the space where you land.

First to arrive at the beach is the winner.

Some of my best fun is with junk.

Fun with Junk

There are always a lot of odds and ends around the house that can be turned into fun things for a few hours. However, don't forget to tidy up after your game and return everything to its right place.

These few suggestions of things to build can all be done by yourself, but it's much more fun if you have a friend over to enjoy it with you, and add their suggestions.

Build a car

You will need:
    cardboard carton
    paper plates
    margarine or yoghurt containers
    felt-tip pens or poster paints
    sticky tape and glue
    scissors

How to make:
The cardboard carton is the basic car body on to which you will build everything. Use the felt-tip pen to draw on the wheels — a paper plate provides the ideal outline for the wheel circles.

Now use the paper plate for your steering wheel. The margarine or yoghurt cartons make great front and rear lights.

Let your imagination run wild and add on all the extras you can think of — like fancy paintwork, a radio plus an aerial. To make it even more authentic find some more paper plates and paint your own road signs.

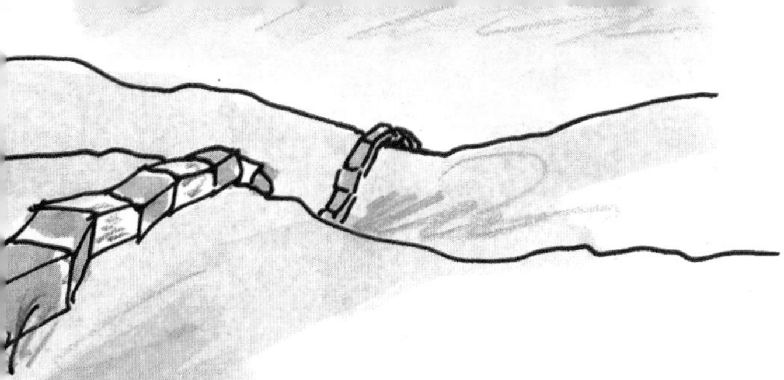

Tunnels

If you find a heap of old supermarket cardboard cartons stored in the back of the garage or laundry, here's a great way to put them to good use.

You will need:

    as many cardboard cartons as you can find
    lots of old newspapers
    sticky tape

How to make:

Open out the tops and bottoms of all the cartons. Set them out in an "S" shape around the room, leaving a small space between each carton.

    The idea is to join the open ends of the cartons together by sticking sheets of newspaper across them (as shown). This allows you to build a longer tunnel.

    Now try and wriggle your way through the tunnel without breaking it to pieces! Keep the sticky tape handy.

Hobby horse

string

You will need:

    all the brooms and mops in the house (one for each person)
    old socks or stockings
    old newspapers or magazines
    string
    cardboard
    felt-tip pens
    needle and cotton
    sticky tape

How to make:

Stuff the old socks or stockings with newspaper, shaping them into a horse's head as much as possible. Attach to the top of the broom handle by tying with string (as shown).

    Cut 2 eye shapes and 2 ear shapes from the cardboard, sew into position and colour in with felt-tip pens.

    Make a mane for your horse by cutting strips of newspaper and gently stitching into place. You can add a set of reins by using string or an old belt.

Food for Winter

Have you noticed that during winter you always feel hungry and want to eat more? This is because your body needs more fuel to help keep it warm.

Try making these tasty snacks to share with your family and friends, and to keep out the cold.

Joan's bitties

These are a savoury, crunchy biscuit which are ideal for enjoying as a pre-dinner snack. *Warning* — watch out for the grown-ups, they love them too!

You will need:
5 pieces of pitta, pocket or unleavened bread
Vegemite or Marmite

How to make:
Carefully split the bread in half, making each piece into 2 thin pieces. Spread moderately thickly with the Vegemite or Marmite.

Cut into odd shapes and bake in a hot oven for about 10 minutes, until crisp. Watch so they don't burn. Allow to cool and store in an airtight jar.

Marshmallows

You will need:
3 tablespoons gelatine
1 cup cold water
4 cups sugar
1½ cups hot water
vanilla
icing sugar
cornflour

How to make:
Soak gelatine in cold water and put to one side. Bring sugar and hot water to the boil. Add soaked gelatine and boil gently for 20 minutes stirring occasionally.

Pour into a bowl, cool and add vanilla, then beat until thick. Wet a slab-cake tin and pour in mixture.

When thoroughly cool, cut into squares and toss in the mixture of icing sugar and cornflour.

For other flavours you can use lemon essence or peppermint essence instead of the vanilla. Or you can split the mixture and have three flavours.

To toast: see page 47.

Pikelets

You will need:
- 1 egg
- 4 tablespoons sugar
- 1 cup self-raising flour
- ¾ cup milk
- 1 tablespoon melted butter

How to make:

Beat the egg and sugar together. Add the flour and milk alternately. Finally, pour in the melted butter.

Grease a frying pan or griddle iron, and heat. Drop in a tablespoon of the mixture, brown on both sides, and place on kitchen paper.

Serve with a choice of butter, jam, honey and cream.

Thick and hearty soup

You will need:

4 cups of stock — made by boiling bones, meat scraps, bacon bones or chicken bones, for an hour, then straining thoroughly

vegetables — any amount and a large variety. This is a good way to use up the last of the vegetables left in the fridge.

How to make:

Combine the stock and vegetables in a large saucepan and bring slowly to the boil until vegetables are well cooked. Add a small amount of salt and pepper if required.

Allow to cool, then mash — a food processor is ideal for this.

Re-heat to serve, with toast on the side. An ideal supper dish in front of the fire, followed by pikelets. Yummy!

Games with Words

This page is full of ideas for that winter day when you and your friends have been told to go and play, "but do be quiet about it!".

You will need to find a pencil for everyone, a pile of writing paper, and a dictionary in case you need to settle an argument!

Hunt the alphabet

For this game you will need to give each player a pair of scissors and one page out of an old newspaper or magazine. You will also need a bottle of glue, but this must be shared by everyone.

The object of this game is for each player to find all the letters of the alphabet, both in capitals and lower case, and paste them in the correct order on a sheet of paper.

If towards the end of the game you are still missing some letters, then trade your newspaper with another player.

The winner is the player who is finished first, with the neatest alphabets!

Growing words

To begin this game choose one of the players' names which everyone then prints at the top of a piece of paper. The idea is to make words grow.

Using the letters at the top of your page each player begins by making two-letter words, then three-letter words, then four and so on.

As an example:

A N N E	A N N E	A N N E	A N N E
N O O X	N O E A	L O O A	G O I A
	D T T T	A T O S	R R G R
		S E N T	E T H T
			E H T H

You score 2 points for each correct two-letter word, 3 points for three-letter words, and so on. No points for repeating a word, or for a word not in the dictionary.

14

Confusing telegrams

Choose one of the players' names and everyone prints this across the top of their page. The idea of this game is for each player to work out a fun telegram message, using each letter of the chosen name as the initial letter for each word of the telegram. They must be kept in the same order.

Here's an example: NICHOLAS

No ice cream have only liquorice after supper.

Mirror letters

Down the side of the page each player lists the letters of the alphabet. The object of this game is to find words containing two of each particular letter together.

To start you off:
A   aardvark
B   bubble
C   account
D   addition
   You can make it easier by allowing proper names, for example: Aaron.
   Score 1 point for each correct answer, plus a bonus point for these difficult letters: A, H, I, J, Q, U, V, W, X, Y and Z.
   You will definitely need the dictionary for this game.

mirror letter

It's for "mind another ringtailed yak."*

* see "confusing telegrams".

How many?

The first player chooses a word which everyone prints across the top of their paper, spacing out the letters. The suggested word could be RAIN.
   Player number 2 suggests a subject, say FOOD. Each player must now list all the foods they can think of beginning with the letters of the word chosen by the first player. For example:

R	A	I	N
raspberries	apples	ice cream	nuts

   Score 1 point for each correct answer. This game can cover all sorts of subjects from car names to book characters. It's hours of fun.

Anagrams

An anagram is a word, or phrase, the letters of which can all be rearranged into another word, or phrase. For example: SEAT can become EATS, TEAS, EAST and so on.
   Choose several words and see how many new words each player can find. Here are a few to begin: POST, ARTS, ASLEEP.
   Make it harder and try a phrase.

Winter Gardening

← a tree in a woolly jumper

Winter is mostly a time of rest for your outdoor garden, however it is the ideal time to try your hand at growing some fun things indoors.

Picture sprouts

Take several sheets of paper towel from the kitchen and place them in a flat, shallow dish.

On a sheet of cardboard, or paper, draw either a cat or a flower, or whatever, cut out the centre of your drawing and throw it away. Now place the sheet of cardboard, or paper, on the paper towels.

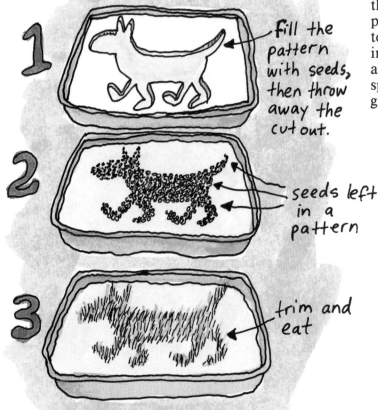

fill the pattern with seeds, then throw away the cut out.

seeds left in a pattern

trim and eat

Sprinkle alfalfa seeds into the cut-out section of the cardboard, then throw it away. Gently water the seeds so as not to disturb the pattern and then place the dish in a warm, sunny spot — a window sill is the ideal place.

Keep your seeds moist and within a week you should have a great pattern growing. Trim them off and use as sandwich fillers.

Vegetable tops

Surprise everyone and offer to prepare the vegetables for dinner! The reason for doing this is so that you can obtain the materials to grow a fun garden.

Carefully cut off the tops of the carrots, parsnips, turnips or onions, leaving at least 10 mm of the vegetable attached to the bottom. Put these carefully to one side.

Next you borrow a shallow dish or plate and cover with cotton wool or several layers of paper towel. Add enough water to moisten them right through.

Now take the vegetable tops and place them, cut side down, on the cotton wool or paper. Keep in a dark place until they begin to shoot then, each day, move them further into the light. Remember to keep them moist at all times and you will end up with a lovely spray of greenery (and some interesting root growth).

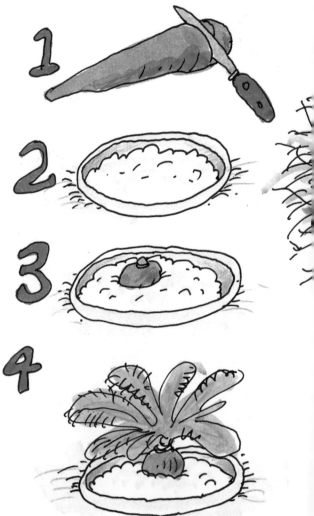

Winter colour

The winter buds, on the bare branches of the trees and shrubs, are the beginnings of the next year's growth carefully wrapped up against the cold and waiting for the warmth of spring to bring them out.

Carefully cut a few branches from a willow or a birch tree and place them in a vase of water. Put the vase in the warmest and if possible, sunniest spot in the house.

Over the next weeks, and you do have to be patient, the buds will slowly open and leaves will appear. Then you will have spring in your house long before it begins in the garden.

Water wonders

The growing of plants in water is called hydroponics. Here is a simple experiment to show how it works.

You will need either a hyacinth bulb or an avocado seed. Find a glass jar with a neck that will fit the hyacinth bulb (as shown). Fill with water, to the base of the bulb. Find a nice, dark but airy place and hide it away. Check at regular intervals, topping up the water.

As soon as the shoots begin to appear move the jar into the light. Now you can watch as the roots grow down into the water and the leaves and flower slowly open on top. Remember to keep that water topped up!

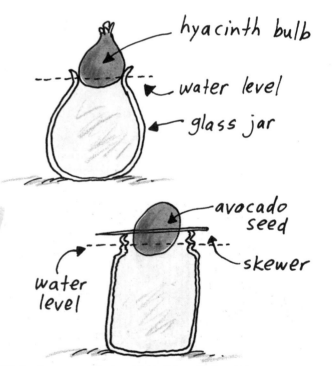

With the avocado seed it doesn't hurt to spear it with a skewer and rest it across the top of a jar (as shown). You can't do this to the hyacinth bulb because you would destroy the flower growing inside.

Treat the avocado the same way as the hyacinth, and watch it grow. If you look after it you'll be surprised at how tall it will reach.

Weather Watch

It's good to watch the weather but never look at the sun.

The weather affects all of us, especially the long, cold days of winter when we are likely to be shut inside for ages (this is the time when we all dream of those lazy, hazy days of summer).

However, winter days shut inside need not be dull or boring. This is a good time to learn about the weather and how to predict what is likely to happen.

To make you feel even colder, why not keep your own daily temperature chart. This will enable you to record the coldest day each week, as well as plotting the coming of spring.

Daily temperature chart

You will need:
>1 large sheet plain paper
>ruler and pencil

How to make:
Draw a chart (as shown) making a range of temperatures down the left side of the page.

Across the top of the page, mark the days and dates for that month. Make a separate chart for each month, this will allow plenty of room on each sheet of paper — it's also easier to mark-up and read.

You will be able to keep track of each day's temperatures by watching the television, or looking up your daily paper, which gives a weather map and temperatures from the previous day.

Another fun thing to do is to keep a weather diary for each day. This gives more details than the temperature chart because you can mark in symbols showing whether it was wet or windy or frosty. The sample diary gives you an idea of the symbols you can use.

Become the weather forecaster for your family by being observant and watching for signs that tell you what is likely to happen. For example:

- Clear, starry skies always mean a chilly, frosty night. The next day will usually be sunny, but cold.
- A low, dark sky and a slightly warm wind usually means that snow is on the way.

Frost experiment

bottle with cork in it
cardboard box
water

You will need:
    1 large cardboard box
    1 glass bottle with cork top

How to set up:
On a cold, frosty night, take the cardboard box outside. In it place the glass bottle filled with water, with the cork firmly in place. Leave for the night. In the morning you will have one broken bottle. This has occurred because water expands as it freezes.

Weather words

Did you know that there are many sayings in our language that reflect our weather?

"I'm snowed under at work."

"I haven't the foggiest idea."

"It's such a cold wind, it's cutting me in half."

"His future is cloudy."

There's a strong wind warning.

19

Winter Sports Trivia

Archery

Archery is one of the oldest sports still being practised. In fact archaeologists have proved it existed over 10 000 years ago.

Archers are called "toxophilites", a word which comes from the Greek *toxon* meaning bow.

The famous battles of Crécy, Agincourt and Poitiers were won by the English using their famous longbow made from the yew trees.

The longbow became so important in England that a law was passed which stated that yew trees must be grown in all cemeteries.

The invention of gunpowder made archers redundant!

Bobsledding

This sport originated in Switzerland about 1890, when wood runners were added to wooden toboggans.

Bobsledding became an internationally recognised sport in 1924, when it was included in the Winter Olympics held at Chamonix, France.

Billiards

The beginnings of billiards is surrounded in mystery. One theory is that it came from the East where it was an out-of-doors sport. When the Crusaders brought it back to England they changed it into "lawn bowls on tables".

King Louis XIV of France took up billiards for his health in 1694, when his doctor told him he needed more exercise.

Croquet

One of the most famous streets in the world, Pall Mall in London, is named after a game that was once played there — palla (ball) and maglio (mallet), known today as croquet.

At one stage during its long history croquet was the butt of some nasty jokes. It was said to be a game that was suitable only for elderly ladies and the vicar.

Ice skating

The first skates were probably made from the shankbone of an animal — sheep, ox, horse or reindeer — and they may have been fastened to the feet with a leather thong.

Archaeologists have found that skates existed in prehistoric times in Asia and Europe. They were certainly used by the Vikings in Scandinavia.

The first reference to ice skating in literature is said to have been in a famous collection of Icelandic sagas. In this the god of winter is described as speeding over the ice on animal bones.

It is claimed that while King Charles II of England was exiled in Holland he learnt to skate.

Skiing

The oldest known pair of skis, in a museum in Stockholm, is thought to be about 5000 years old.

The world's first skis, like the world's first skates, were probably made from the bones of large animals.

In ancient times, the people of northern Europe worshipped the goddess of skiing. Her name was Skadi and legend states that she could shoot wild animals with her bow and arrows while travelling on her snow shoes.

Australia, not Switzerland or Austria, is the birthplace of skiing as a sport. It began in the snowfields near Kiandra, where the Norwegian gold miners came in the 1860s.

Another Australian contribution to the world of skiing is the word *moko*, a term for the wax used on skis. It's an Australian abbreviation of the words "more go".

Soccer

Soccer, as it is played today, is a direct descendent of the ancient "mêlées" played in England, in which a round or oval object was kicked or punched into a goal.

In London, in October 1863, a group of clubs came together to form "The Football Association" and to draw up a unified code.

So Association Football came into being, but student slang created the term "soccer" using the letters S, O, and C as their base.

Table tennis

Table tennis was devised as a kind of miniature tennis at the end of last century, but it really has its beginnings in 12th century Royal Tennis.

King George VI had a table set up at Balmoral Castle during World War II so that his daughters, the young Princess Elizabeth and Princess Margaret, could enjoy the game.

Other famous people who have enjoyed a game include the Shah of Persia, Pundit Nehru and King Farouk of Egypt.

When the game was first marketed, by sporting goods companies, it came out with a variety of names: Gossima; Whiff Whaff; Flim Flam and of course Ping-Pong.

Winter Walks

Winter walks will be very different in various parts of the world. If you live in the tropics or sub-tropics, winter is the best time of the year to be outdoors, so you will need our *Summer Fun Book* for your winter activities.

However, most of us live in a temperate (or even colder) climate, so winter walks will mean wrapping up well against the cold.

Walking on a clear winter day can often be far more enjoyable than during the heat of a summer day. However, always remember that the days are much shorter, so don't set out on a long walk without making sure you can be home well before the light begins to fade.

Winter trees

During winter you will be able to see more on your walks because so many trees are deciduous (they lose their leaves in autumn, and grow new ones each spring). The ones that don't lose their leaves are called evergreens.

How many of these trees can you find and identify on a winter walk?

Borrow some books from your local library and discover more about the trees in your area.

Evergreens:

Deciduous:

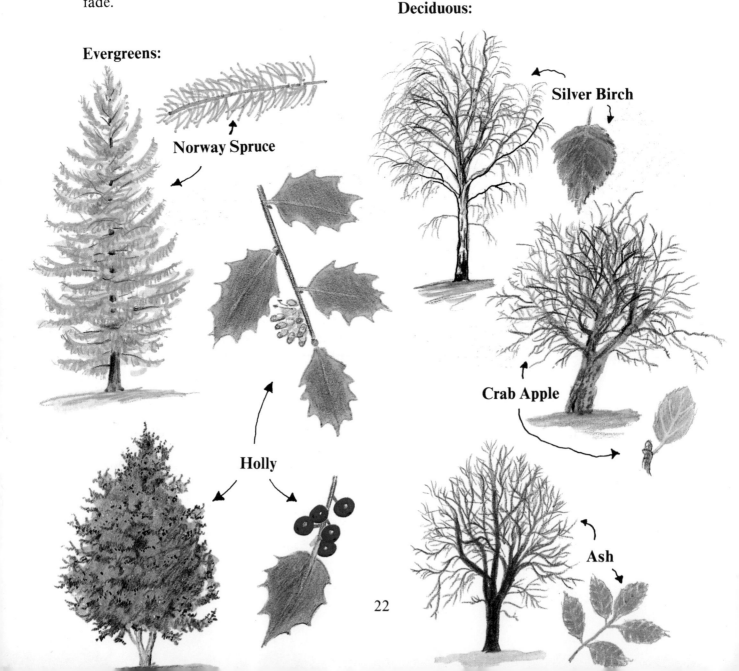

Norway Spruce

Silver Birch

Holly

Crab Apple

Ash

22

Collecting cones

Another interesting thing to do on a winter walk is to collect cones. They come in dozens of different shapes and sizes and can be used for many things.

Firstly, see how many you can identify. Here are a few to help you start, but you will need to use your library for more details.

After you have identified the cones you collected they can then be used in various ways:

- they are great for burning in an open fire-place — but be careful, they spit a lot
- they can be spray painted and used as Christmas decorations
- they can be turned into bird feeders (see page 25)
- they make an excellent place to grow orchids and bromeliads.

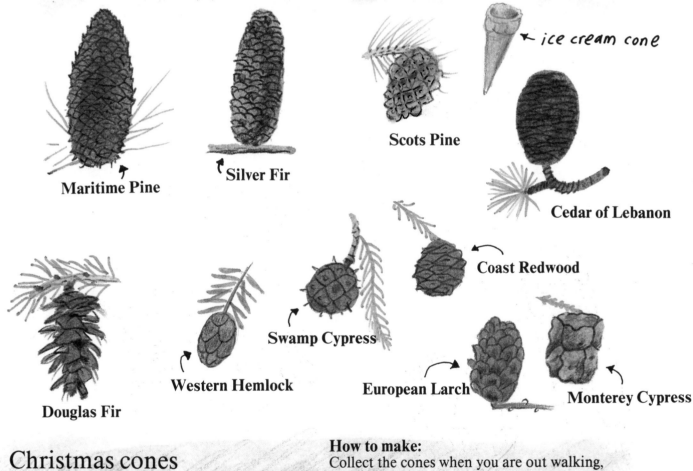

Maritime Pine

Silver Fir

Scots Pine

← ice cream cone

Cedar of Lebanon

Coast Redwood

Douglas Fir

Western Hemlock

Swamp Cypress

European Larch

Monterey Cypress

Christmas cones

You will need:
    10 cones various shapes
    1 spray can of paint (any colour, but silver, red and green are the best Christmas colours)

How to make:
Collect the cones when you are out walking, choosing the most interesting and unusual shapes — some open and some closed.

Buy a can of spray paint, then ask someone to help you — they can hold the cone steady while you spray the tip. Allow them to dry thoroughly before storing them for Christmas.

Feed the Birds

It has been estimated that only half the birds born during spring will live a full year. One of their enemies is winter and we can help them through this time by adding to their food supply during those months when their normal sources have disappeared.

By making a few bird feeders, and hanging them well out of the reach of cats, you will get to know your local birds and how they behave.

During winter many of the insects which the birds normally feed on will disappear. One way of replacing this in their diet is to make bird feeders that include unsalted peanuts and fats. Here are a couple of suggestions:

Fat feeders

You will need:
- 1 empty yoghurt container
- 1 lump of fat
- birdseed
- 1 length of soft wire

How to make:
Melt down the fat and add a handful of birdseed. Pour into the yoghurt container. Allow to cool. Before the mixture has hardened, place the wire in the centre (as shown) leaving enough to hook over a small branch. Place in fridge and allow to set hard. When solid, scoop out of the pot by running a knife around the edge. It is now ready to hang outside.

Have you been feeding the birds again, Simon?

yoghurt container

wire bent into this shape

1

2 bird seed mixed into the fat

3

4

24

Coconut feeder

You should be able to buy coconuts from your fruitshop almost all the year round. The birds will enjoy the white flesh and pick it clean.

You will need:
>   coconut
>   saw
>   drill and bit
>   length of soft wire
>   an adult to help you

How to make:
Saw the coconut in half — you may need someone to hold it. (If you haven't a saw, a careful hit with a hammer should split it into two pieces.) You only need one half to make a feeder so you can either eat the other half yourself or make two feeders.

Ask an adult to drill 2 holes near the top of one half of the coconut on opposite sides and drill another hole for drainage in the bottom of the shell.

Thread soft wire through the holes and twist each end back on itself as shown. Hang the feeder on a branch and wait for the birds to find it.

Once the birds have pecked out all the white flesh, you can refill the shell with the same mixture that you made for the Fat Feeder (see opposite page).

drill hole

drill hole

If you are fortunate enough to have a cat-proof feeding tray in your garden, then choose the food you leave out with thought and care, because you could end up doing the birds a great deal of harm.

Here are a few tips:

• too much bread and sugar can lead to an unbalanced diet and cause deformities in their young
• if leaving something sweet, a little sugar is better than honey — honey ferments
• meat has too much phosphorous and very little calcium.

If in doubt, phone your local zoo. We have found that many of the zoos recommend canned dog food or dried cat food as alternatives, and either will give the birds a change in their diet.

Remember that feeding trays need to be cleaned *every* day to get rid of the uneaten food which rots very quickly, especially if it's been raining.

Birds in winter

During winter the kittiwake, one of the gull family, will spend all its time at sea, feeding at the surface on fish and marine animals.

Deep snow and extreme cold can be disastrous for birds. To reduce heat loss they fluff out their feathers, and to save energy they will sit quietly on a perch.

The birds' lives are governed by the annual cycle of the seasons. There is a time of plenty — that is the summer of the temperate regions and the wet season of the tropics — followed by a period of shortage — the winter or dry season. So the birds gear their lives to the seasons.

Grow Your Own Ants

During winter many insects hibernate, they prefer to sleep through the cold weather rather than try and live through it. If you wander around your garden you are likely to find cocoons spun by caterpillars. By wrapping themselves up carefully, these insects can stay dry and safe from the winter weather.

Look for these cocoons in your garden, but don't disturb them, just watch them throughout the winter and see what happens in spring.

Do Not Disturb

Winter is also a hard time for bees. They will use up their stored honey to stay alive, so a beekeeper will feed them extra sugar and water so that they won't eat up all his profits.

Ants will look for a dry place to nest during these cold months. If there is an extremely wet period you will notice the ants moving into your home — they hate being too wet.

It's very easy to build your own ant farm and watch them construct their numerous tunnels. If you are clever enough to catch a Queen ant, then they will build a special chamber for her and the eggs.

a bee in a bee-sized woolly jumper

an ant in a person-sized woolly jumper

"Hop in. It's for you."

Building an ant farm

You will need:

1 large glass bottle, with lid
hammer and nail
dessert spoon

How to make:

Thoroughly wash and dry the bottle, inside and out, making sure you remove all labels. With the hammer and nail, carefully punch air holes in the lid, but not too large — you don't want your ants escaping!

Fill the bottle with a light soil. Now go ant hunting, taking your bottle with its lid, and the dessert spoon. The spoon is used to carefully dig up the ants and place them in the bottle.

When you have collected 20 to 30 ants, screw the lid on and head for home. Place the bottle where you can watch the ants at work. Slowly they will begin to tunnel, and many of the tunnels will be down the side of the bottle, so you will have a clear view of how they work.

Remember to feed them crumbs of bread and other food scraps, but not enough to make your ant farm smelly — they only eat a small amount so don't overfeed! Also, an occasional few drops of water, but don't drown them — they don't like too much water.

1. Hammer very small holes in the lid.

2. put the soil in.

one or two drops of water on a leaf

3. food

"Have you seen my ant farm anywhere?"

27

Jokes and Puzzles

Jokes

Q When is a boat like a heap of snow?
A When it's adrift.

Q Which animal is it best to be on a cold day?
A A little otter.

Q What goes "croak, croak" when it's misty?
A A froghorn.

Q What is a weather forecaster's favourite game?
A Draughts.

Q What lies at the bottom of the ocean shaking?
A A nervous wreck.

Q Where do snowmen go to dance?
A A snowball.

Hidden words

There is a winter word hidden in each of these sentences. Can you find it? Example: It's *now* I need the car, not tomorrow.

Answer: snow.

1 The zoo gives free zebra rides on Saturdays.
2 Peggy guesses we ate Robert's chocolates.
3 The desk at Essen's store is just what I need.
4 Jane saw, in downtown Sydney, a coat she loved.
5 This car from the hire company is dirty.

Here's another one. This is a mirror image addition which gives you the same answer.

1 2 3 4 5 6 7 8 9	9 8 7 6 5 4 3 2 1
1 2 3 4 5 6 7 8	8 7 6 5 4 3 2 1
1 2 3 4 5 6 7	7 6 5 4 3 2 1
1 2 3 4 5 6	6 5 4 3 2 1
1 2 3 4 5	5 4 3 2 1
1 2 3 4	4 3 2 1
1 2 3	3 2 1
1 2	2 1
1	1
1 0 8 3 6 7 6 2 6 9	1 0 8 3 6 7 6 2 6 9

Fun with numbers

Have you noticed that in the nine times table all the answers add up to nine?

1 x 9 = 9
2 x 9 = 18 (1 + 8 = 9)
3 x 9 = 27 (2 + 7 = 9)
4 x 9 = 36 (3 + 6 = 9)
5 x 9 = 45 (4 + 5 = 9)

Fun, isn't it? Check out the others yourself.

Test your maths skills on this set of empty boxes. You have to write the correct number in each box so that no matter which way you add up your answer will always be 18.

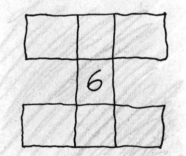

(Answers: freeze, sweater, skates, wind, scarf)

(Answer: Top row 7,8,3. Bottom row 9,4,5)

29

What To Do When There's Nothing To Do

If it's one of those cold, wet winter days and there are several of you in the house feeling bored, then head for the kitchen and ask an older person to help you set up your own "taste test" survey.

You will have seen these "taste tests" happening in supermarkets, when they set out a number of different brands of the same product and then invite people to try them all and say which one they like best, and why.

This may sound easy, but it's harder than you think, because the way you judge a flavour is also influenced by the way the product looks, feels and smells.

There are dozens and dozens of different flavours in the things we eat, all made by the way we taste and smell them. However, there are actually only four different tastes: sweet, sour, bitter and salty.

These tastes are all recognised by the 9000 tastebuds that sit on the top of your tongue! What is interesting is that the four tastes are tasted on different parts of your tongue.

This is how your tongue tastes:

- sweet on the tip
- salty on the sides and tip
- sour further back on the sides
- bitter right at the back.

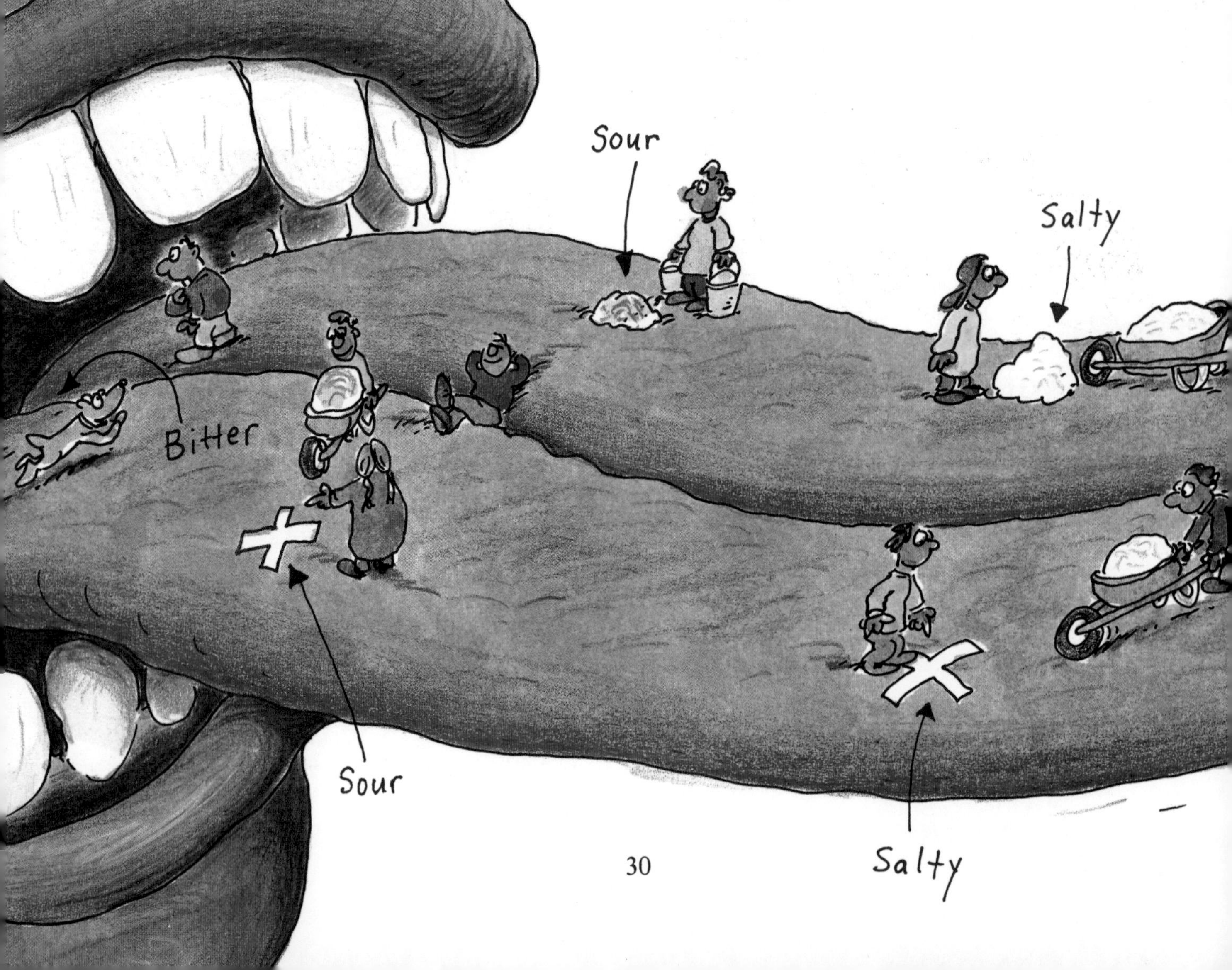

Sour

Salty

Bitter

Sour

Salty

Test your 9000 tastebuds

You will need:
- 4 cups
- 1 spoonful of sugar (sweet)
- 1 spoonful of salt (salty)
- 1 spoonful of vinegar (sour)
- 1 spoonful of instant coffee (bitter)
- 1 eye-dropper (or your finger)

How to test:
Fill each cup with water. Stir the sugar into one, the salt into another and so on. You now have your 4 tastes.

Using the eye-dropper, or the top of your finger, place a small drop of each liquid onto the different parts of your tongue and see if you can taste them.

The no-one nose test

This is not just a taste-test, it also makes a great party game.

You need at least 3 players for this game, more if possible, plus 1 adult to help. Choose 1 player, who is "it", and send them out of the room while the game is set up.

Place 5 or 6 items to be tasted on plates, things like a piece of apple, flour, honey, salt, cheese, anything that can be eaten which will not burn or make the player choke.

This nose needs a peg on it.

Salty

Sweet

The player who is "it" must be blindfolded and have a clothes-peg very gently placed on their nose before being brought into the room. Sit the player at the table with the plates and see how many tastes they can guess. One point for each correct answer.

Now another player is chosen, plus a whole new range of tastes to test. This is repeated until everyone has a turn and a winner is found.

31

Collectors' Items

I really recommend page 24.

Collecting things is fun, but collections need to be kept organised or there are likely to be complaints from the other members of your family.

The long, cold winter afternoons are the ideal time to sort out all those interesting things collected during the summer, but which you never got round to sorting out or identifying.

All collectors do a lot of looking and picking-up, and there are times when you need both hands free to examine something closely. So why not make yourself these few collection aids?

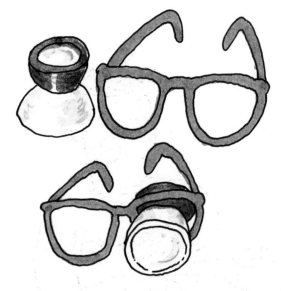

Magnifying spectacles

A magnifying glass is always an essential tool for a collector, and it is not an expensive item to buy — most stamp shops carry a good choice. However, a magnifying glass has to be held in one hand which can be a nuisance at times, so why not make yourself a pair of magnifying spectacles.

All you need is an old pair of spectacles — old sunglasses will do — and your new magnifying glass.

Take both lenses out of the spectacles and replace one side with the lense from your new magnifying glass. It can be held firmly in place by using a plastic glue (as shown).

Specimen holder

Another easy-to-make and useful item for a collector is a specimen holder.

All you need is a milk bottle filled with earth, with a stick placed firmly in it. Before putting the stick in place tie a plastic peg to the top (as shown). Attach firmly by winding a piece of string around several times and tying off with a reef knot.

Reef knot

clothes peg

1 2
how to tie a reef knot
3 4

Collection containers

An ideal way to store collections of small things, like tiny shells, is to make a set of drawers out of matchboxes.

Collect 10 matchboxes and set them up in 2 piles of 5 (as shown). Carefully glue together starting with the bottom pair. When dry and firmly stuck together, take out each tray and loosely sew a button on the front. This will make the opening of the drawers much easier.

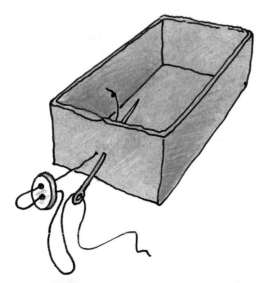

Collection trivia

A person who collects stamps is called a philatelist.

A person who collects coins and medals is called a numismatist and numismatologist.

A person who collects teddy bears is called an arctophile.

Coin collectors have a language of their own when it comes to describing their coins:

- "fair" means that the coins can just about be identified
- "good" means very worn, but the design is still visible in outline
- "very good" means the design shows well, but the detail is worn
- "fine" means it shows signs of wear.

I agree with the bird at the top of the opposite page.

The popular Chinese-style willow pattern china comes from Staffordshire in England — it never came from China. Even the legend that the picture tells of the beautiful Chinese girl running away with her father's poor secretary, and both being chased by the father, has nothing to do with China. It was made up in England during the 19th century.

The world's smallest stamps were printed between 1863 and 1866, in Bolivia. They were 8 x 9.5 mm (0.31 x 0.37 inches).

That's how small 8 x 9.5mm is.

Matchstick Puzzles

Like *Games with Words* on page 14, these matchstick puzzles are ideal when you and your friends have been told to go and play a quiet game. All you need to take with you is a box of used matches.

Now settle down and see how many of these brain-teasers you can solve. Try and not look at the answers, which are on page 48, until everyone has had time to work them out.

Farmer puzzle

You will need 12 matches for each player arranged like this:

Each player is a farmer owning 4 cows. The matchsticks represent the fenced fields, and the fences are movable. In each field there is 1 cow.

Puzzle 1
Unfortunately 1 cow dies. Rearrange the fences so that the remaining 3 cows have a square field each. There must be no matchsticks left over.

Puzzle 2
A second cow dies! To get more money you sell 2 fences. Go back to the original arrangement and, with 10 matchsticks, make 2 square fields for your last 2 cows. (Clue: there's a catch!)

Perfect match

For this puzzle each player will need 13 matchsticks set out in this triangular design:

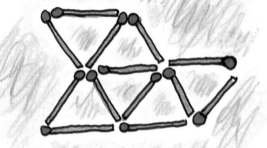

The challenge is to remove 3 matchsticks and end up with 3 triangles.

Here's a hard one. How do you move one match to make a flame?

34

Triangle tricks

Give each player 9 matchsticks. Make a triangle from 3 of the matchsticks. That was easy, everyone should have managed that!

Having used 3 matchsticks to make 1 triangle, there will be no problems in making 3 triangles from the 9 matchsticks.

Now to the problem — make 4 triangles out of the 9 matchsticks.

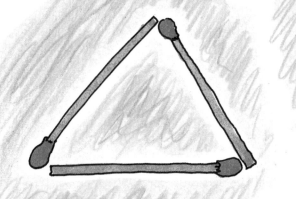

Grid puzzle

Set out 12 matchsticks in the following pattern:

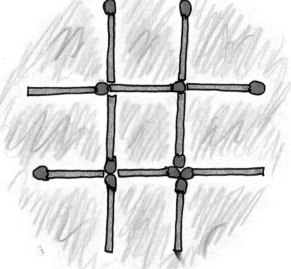

The idea is to move 3 matchsticks to produce 3 identical squares. (There are several answers.)

A difficult one

Each player needs 24 matchsticks. First set out 16 matches in a large "L" shape, as shown:

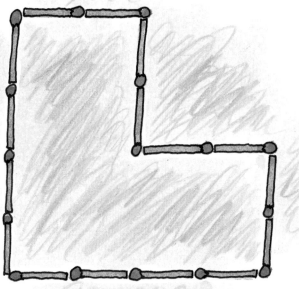

Now, with the 8 spare matchsticks, construct 4 "Ls" within the big "L". Take your time, this one is difficult.

A trick one

See how bright you are. Give each player 4 matchsticks and set out *exactly* as shown:

Now, make a square by moving only 1 matchstick. If anyone solves this, they deserve a special prize!

Sketching Indoors

If you want to try your hand at sketching, then the first thing you must do is learn how to *look*. By looking you are learning the basic skill of drawing.

We will try and give you a few pointers on how and where to start with pencil sketching — and we have chosen indoors because it is winter — later you can be more adventurous, experimenting with other mediums like charcoal, crayon or pen and ink, and other subject matters both indoors and outdoors.

Know your pencils

The first step is to "know" the pencils you will be using and what they are capable of producing.

Pencils can be brought in a range from the very hard, light 6H through to the soft, dark 6B. It's the Bs that are the most useful, giving you a good range when it comes to shadings and lines.

Choose your paper

Until you are certain you are going to be doing a lot of sketching, don't rush out and buy lots of expensive sketching pads.

For pencil work buy 1 sketch pad with a grainy surface. Ask the shopkeeper's advice. Also try your pencils out on cardboard or coloured paper that you find around your home. By trying these different surfaces you will become aware of the various effects you can create.

Lines and shades

Having collected your various pencils and papers together it's now time to try them out. Taking a sheet of grainy paper, choose a light, hard pencil, say a 2H and a dark, soft pencil, a 2B. Now try drawing the following type of line, once with each pencil, side by side, down your page:

- thick
- thin
- wavy
- broken
- woolly
- delicate

Different types of shading

using a finger to smudge the shading

36

Already you will be seeing the difference in your pencils. Now do those same lines again, but this time do them quickly. Then try them a third time, altering the pressure you normally use.

The next step to try is shading. Shading allows you to give the feeling of depth to your sketching, bringing it to life as you create shadows, light or shade.

Take a soft 3B pencil and draw a series of lines close together, alter the pressure and watch what happens. You will see the shadows come and go (as shown). Now try this with a curved line. Keep practising until you are sure you know what you can make your pencil do.

Using a soft 5B or 6B pencil draw a few fluffy clouds (as shown — or look out of your window for reference!). With your finger try smudging the edges — fun isn't it and a great effect! Next create the cloud's shadow underneath by colouring in the area solidly, using the side of the pencil — hold it firmly.

Light and shadow

One of the best ways to learn to sketch is to begin with a *still life*. Go to the kitchen and ask to borrow a couple of boxes and tins from the food cupboard, and an orange or apple as well.

Set a box up on your desk with a strong light (a desk lamp is ideal) on one side. Now look carefully at these 3 points:

- the direction of the light
- notice the strongest shapes
- study the edges of the shadows.

Move the desk light around, watching the shadows change, and don't forget to watch the "cast shadow" on your desk top.

Try your hand at sketching the box with the light in 3 different positions. Put the box to one side and bring out the orange. Again try the 3 sketches.

There are a couple of points to notice with the orange:

- the shadow is darkest near the light source
- the shadow gets lighter the further it moves from the light source.

smudged pencil

Using the side of the pencil

One way to set up a still life with a light source

Have a go!

With the boxes, tins and fruit borrowed from the kitchen, set up an attractive *still life* design. Take your time, look at it carefully and place the light in the right position.

Now, with your sketch pad and selection of pencils, you are ready to go. Good luck. See if you can do as well as our artist.

37

Woodwork for Winter

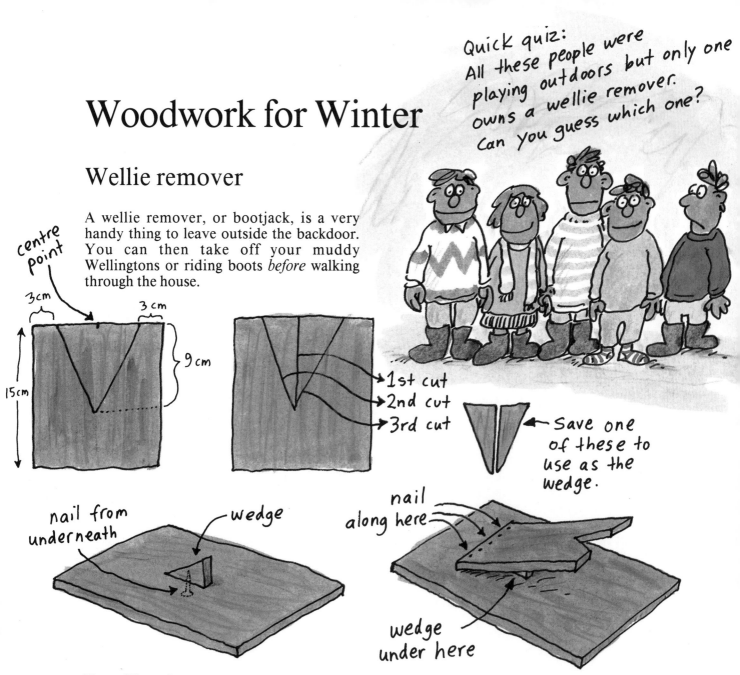

Quick quiz:
All these people were playing outdoors but only one owns a wellie remover. Can you guess which one?

Wellie remover

A wellie remover, or bootjack, is a very handy thing to leave outside the backdoor. You can then take off your muddy Wellingtons or riding boots *before* walking through the house.

centre point

3cm

3 cm

9 cm

15cm

1st cut
2nd cut
3rd cut

Save one of these to use as the wedge.

nail from underneath

wedge

nail along here

wedge under here

You will need:

- 1 piece of soft wood 40 x 20 x 1 cm
- 1 piece of soft wood 15 x 15 x 1 cm
- nails
- hammer
- pencil
- ruler
- saw

How to make:

On the smaller piece of wood carefully mark the centre of 1 side, then 3 cm in from each side. From your centre point mark down 9 cm. With your pencil and ruler join up these points (as shown).

Ask someone to help and get them to hold this piece of wood while you saw. First cut from the centre point down to the 9 cm mark. Next cut the angle across from the 3 cm marks to the 9 cm point. You will end up with 2 small wedges of wood (save these) and a "V" shape in your piece of wood.

Take the larger piece of wood and with your ruler find its centre point. At this point nail on one of the wedges you saved from the smaller piece (as shown).

Take the shorter piece of wood and lay it on the wedge, with the V shape at the higher end. Attach with the nails.

How to use:

Place the heel of the boot in the "V" shape, keeping the other foot on the end of the wood. Pull your foot out of the boot.

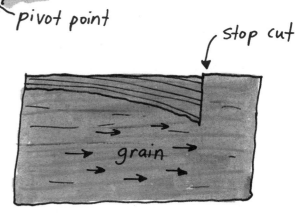

stop cut

**sharp edge.
Always aim the
sharp edge away
from your fingers.**

pivot point

Whittling

This is a skill best learnt by trial and error, but here are a few tips to help you get started.

Always work with soft wood, such as pine. Use a small-bladed *sharp* knife that you must keep sharp.

Begin with simple shapes. Use a soft pencil to mark out these shapes on all sides of your block of wood. Always cut with the grain, from the thickest portion of the wood to the thinnest. Start by roughly carving out your shape then gradually add the details.

To stop your cut at a particular point, make a sharp cut across the grain (as shown) and then work in shallow cuts, shaving the wood away gradually.

For good control of your knife, use your thumb as a pivot point, pushing the blade away from you (as shown).

Sharpening knives

To keep your knife sharp use a sharpening stone that has both a coarse and a smooth side. Oil the stone with a light mineral oil.

Place the sharpening stone, smooth side up, lengthwise in front of you. Always use both hands — one to hold the stone firmly, the other to hold the knife. With this in mind, place the heel of the knife blade on the stone, so that the sharp edge is at an angle of between 15° and 20° to the stone.

stop cut

grain

Polishing wood

There are many ways to polish wood, but the most practical to use on anything you have whittled is polyurethane or acrylic varnish spray, or furniture wax.

If using furniture wax begin by lightly sanding the wood to a smooth finish, using a fine sandpaper or steelwool. Then rub in the wax and polish with a soft cloth, using plenty of elbow grease.

If using the polyurethane or acrylic varnish, sand the wood as for waxing, then follow the directions on the can.

sharp edge   **sharp edge**   **1**   **2**   **3**   **sharp edge**

Pressing with both hands draw the blade in an arc across the stone. Flip the blade and do in reverse. Repeat until the knife is sharp. Follow the diagrams.

The only time you use the coarse side of the stone is when the blade is badly dulled. Always wipe off your stone before putting it away.

Things to Make

Periscope for peeping

Periscopes are very handy, especially when you want to see around a corner, or over the heads of a crowd of people.

You will need:

> 1 piece of strong cardboard 30 x 30 cm
> 2 small hand mirrors
> ruler
> scissors
> sticky tape
> protractor or carpenters' square

a very fat man using a periscope to locate his feet

mirror taped into position

tape

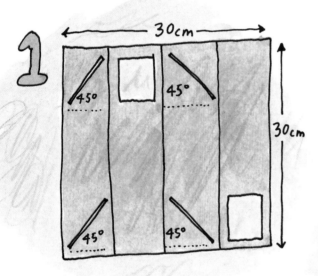

You can use it to see over a wall.

45°   45°

30cm

30cm

45°   45°

using the ruler to help fold along a straight line

How to make:
Divide the cardboard into 4 equal parts by drawing 3 lines (as shown). Cut out 2 squares 5 x 5 cm in the position shown. Measure the thickness of your mirrors then carefully cut 4 strips at 45° angle to the edge of the cardboard (as shown).

Using the ruler, bend the cardboard along the lines and fold into a square and secure together with sticky tape.

Gently slide the mirrors into slots with 1 facing upwards and 1 downwards. Secure the mirrors into position with sticky tape.

Make a fossil

Real fossils take millions of years to form, here is a way to have them instantly!

You will need:
- leaves, feathers, shells
- plaster of Paris
- plastic ice cream container
- small tray of sand
- wire or string
- water

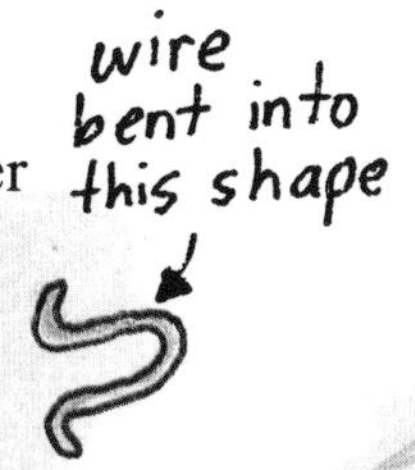

wire bent into this shape

How to make:

Into the tray of sand place a leaf or feather or shell. In the ice cream container, mix the plaster of Paris with the water until you have a creamy substance. Don't mix too much because it doesn't keep, and only mix it as you are about to use because it sets very quickly.

Pour the mixture over the leaf and, while it is still wet, set a loop of wire (or string) to be used to hang it up (when dry).

It will be set in about 30 minutes, but leave until the next day when it will be really hard.

Remove from sand tray and gently clean off grains of sand. You can paint it with your watercolours to make it look old.

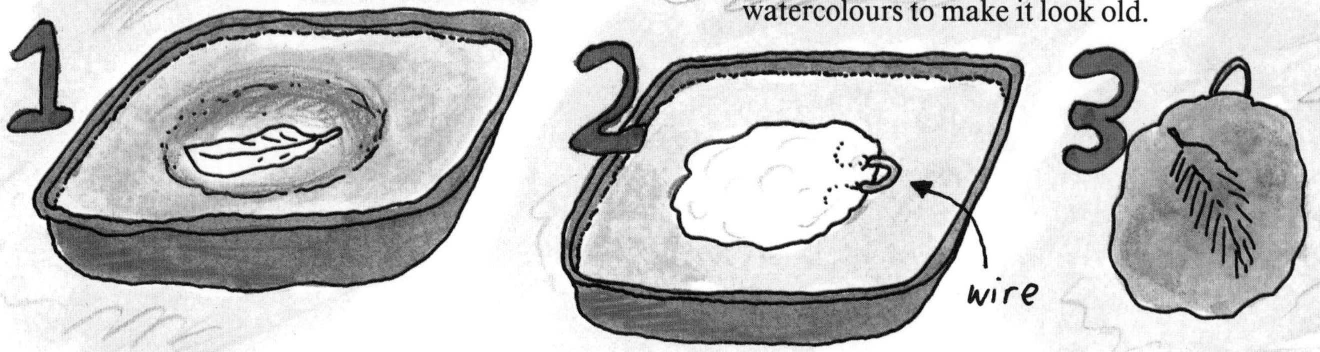

1

2

wire

3

A winter snake

You will need:
- 1 piece of cardboard 30 x 30 cm
- scissors
- coloured pencils
- length of string
- sticky tape

How to make:

On the cardboard draw a spiral (as shown), try and keep it the same width. Carefully cut along the lines of the spiral and open out.

Now colour your snake in a fancy design of stripes and dots. Don't forget to give it a pair of eyes.

Attach the string through the centre of the head, tying firmly behind and securing with a piece of sticky tape.

Hang your snake above the heater in your bedroom and you will be able to watch it spin around as the hot air rises.

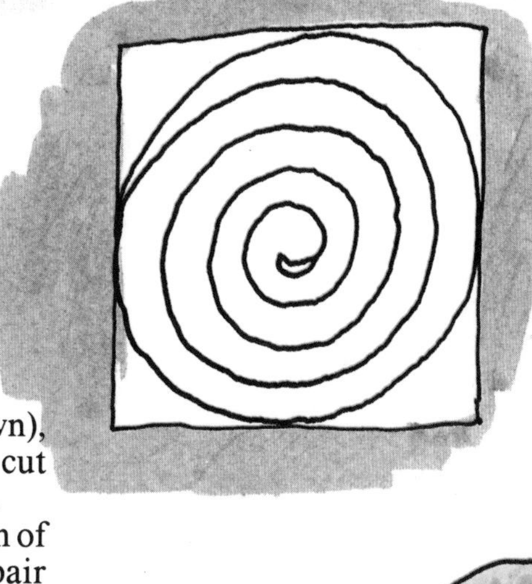

using tape to hold the string

Prints from Plants

Plants can be used in numerous ways to create interesting prints. These can be made into posters for your bedroom wall, or as a present for a friend. They can also be used to make wrapping paper or gift cards.

Always decide what you are making *before* you begin your print, because a poster, wall chart or card will need to be done on cardboard, whereas wrapping paper is best printed on lining paper. If you are doing prints or rubbings to add to your nature book, then you will use a sheet of paper out of the book.

Mushroom patterns

You will need:
>   several ripe mushrooms
>   paper or cardboard
>   can of hairspray or artist's fixative

How to make:
Take the mushrooms, which should be open like an umbrella, and carefully remove the stalk either by twisting or cutting it off (this is not needed).

Place the cap of each mushroom upside down on your sheet of cardboard or paper. Arrange all the caps into the design you require. Leave them undisturbed for at least 12 to 18 hours. What happens is that the spores of the mushrooms will be released onto the paper and each will have a distinctive pattern.

When you lift them off be *very* careful not to blow them or shake them — they will vanish very quickly, especially if you sneeze! Hold the hairspray or artist's fixative well away and spray them gently. This will fix your pattern to the paper.

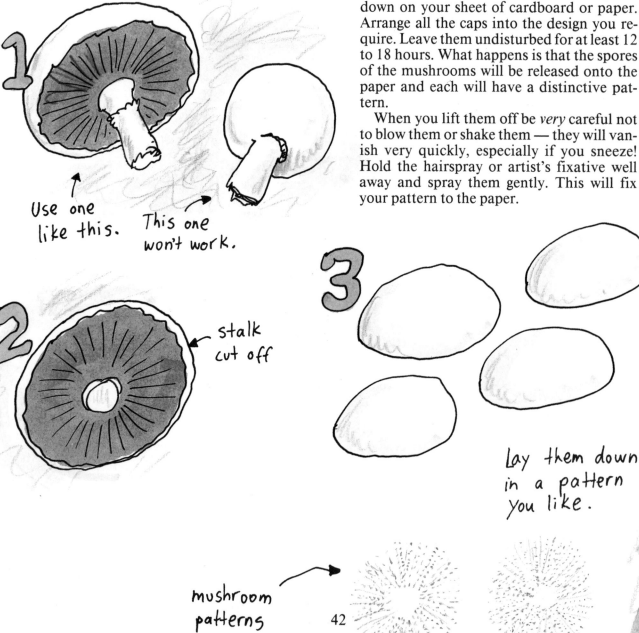

Use one like this.

This one won't work.

stalk cut off

Lay them down in a pattern you like.

mushroom patterns

42

Leaf prints

You will need:
>   leaves of various shapes
>   paper or cardboard
>   aerosol paints (various colours)
>   sticky tape

How to make:
Arrange leaves in a design on the paper or cardboard, attaching with a small circle of sticky tape behind each leaf. Decide on the colour you will spray each leaf. Carefully spray. When dry remove the leaves and there you will have a fabulous overall leaf design.

sticky tape under the leaf

Leaf rubbings

You will need:
>   several dry leaves
>   sheet of thin paper
>   soft 3B pencil
>   writing pad

How to make:
Place a leaf on the writing pad, put the thin sheet of paper over the leaf. Carefully rub the pencil over the thin paper and watch the shape of the leaf appear. This needs a lot of patience and you may have to have several goes before you achieve a good, clear rubbing. Remember to identify each leaf.

place the leaf on the writing pad.

thin paper on top

Carefully shade over with pencil.

You get something like this.

43

A-Z of Surviving Winter

Winter can be a time of coughs and colds and draughty corners, so try these few survival tips to help you make it through to summer.

Chilblains

Don't think that chilblains only happen when the temperature drops below freezing — this just isn't true. Exposure to damp and cold are one of the main causes, along with poor circulation of the blood.

Chilblains usually affect the fingers, toes, ears and nose, so to prevent them always wrap-up well in protective clothing and woollen gloves and socks, and a hat that covers the tips of your ears.

If you do happen to have chilblains *don't* warm them in front of a heater. Warm them slowly and keep them dry. Your chemist may be able to suggest a soothing cream.

Cold sores

Cold sores, or fever blisters, will often appear when you have a cold. They are uncomfortable and sometimes painful, but they will dry up in about 10 days to 3 weeks.

Apply an ice-cold compress 4 or 5 times a day, and don't rub your eyes because you could transfer the infection. Exposure to wind and sun can cause them to flare up, so if you have to go outside, cover up.

Colds

So you've caught a cold! Well, there's no cure for it, all you can do is relieve the symptoms and know it will probably be a week before you're feeling well again.

Rest is important as it allows the body time to fight the virus. Drink lots of liquids.

If your nose is very congested then breathe a hot water vapour under a towel over a basin. Hot drinks will soothe a sore throat, but the best cure of all is lots of rest and sleep.

44

Draught stopper

It's amazing how warm paper can be. If you are out hiking or camping and it suddenly turns very cold, try making these 'draught stopper' trousers.

You will need:
>   newspaper or brown paper
>   scissors
>   sticky tape

How to make:
Place 2 sheets of paper (one on top of the other) flat on the ground, then lay a pair of your trousers on top. Carefully cut out the shape of your trousers, leaving a wide margin around the edges (as shown).

Sticky-tape together (as shown) and wear them over your underwear, with your other trousers over the top. You will soon warm up.

Frostbite

This can occur when parts of the body freeze at −10°C or below, so if you are out winter hiking or camping be extremely careful and prevent it from happening.

Frostbite is extremely painful. The affected area looks white and is hard to the touch. You must seek professional help, but until that is available you can warm the area with lukewarm water — it must NOT be hotter than blood temperature. Don't rub, just pat it dry, then gently wrap in sterile gauze bandages. If moving a patient to hospital from a campsite, make certain that the affected area doesn't refreeze.

Hypothermia

This is a condition that occurs when the body temperature drops below 35°C (the normal temperature, at which our body operates best, is 37°C).

Hypothermia is likely to occur when it's very cold — in wind, snow, rain or on water — and it could happen if you are winter camping or boating in these conditions, and not wearing suitable clothing.

Be aware that it can happen and watch for shivering, pale cold skin, clumsiness, confusion and lethargy.

Seek medical help and, while waiting, gently warm the patient. Provide shelter from wind and remove wet clothing, replacing it with dry warm clothes, then wrap them in a blanket or sleeping bag. A warm drink such as milk or cocoa will be a comfort.

Paper logs

Save money on your fuel bills by making your own logs using up all the old newspapers lying around the house and cluttering up the garage.

They work well in open fireplaces and in most wood stoves, but check the maker's manual before feeding them in just in case they aren't suitable!

masking tape

You will need:
lots of dry black-and-white newspapers (colour is printed on a different paper which doesn't work as fuel logs)
1 dowel stick 30 cm long
masking tape

How to make:
Tightly roll the newspapers around the dowel stick, until you have a roll about 12 cm in diameter. Stick the ends down with the masking tape and remove the dowel ready to start your next paper log.

The dowel leaves a hole right through the middle of your paper log, which helps it to burn.

Experiment by using just a couple of your paper logs with wooden logs, until you find how many of each you need to burn together to give you a warm fire.

Have you seen today's paper anywhere?

Popping corn

Popcorn is a special treat to save for a winter's night in front of an open fire, or when you're snuggled up in bed reading a good book.

Your popcorn's "popability" depends on how much moisture is retained in the raw kernels. To keep this moisture just right you need to store them in an airtight jar in the refrigerator.

You will need:
heavy saucepan with lid
¼ cup cooking oil
½ cup popping corn kernels (this will give you about 14 cups of popcorn)
salt and melted butter

How to make:
Pre-heat the pan for 1 minute then add the cooking oil. Add enough corn kernels to cover the bottom of the pan. Put on the lid and cook over a medium to high heat, shaking the pan gently until the kernels stop popping. From time to time lift the lid a little to let out the steam.

Pour the popped corn into a large bowl and sprinkle with the salt and melted butter. You might like to try mixed herbs instead of salt.

Toasted marshmallows

For these you must have an open fireplace, or be out camping and have your camp fire burning low.

You will need:
plenty of marshmallows (see page 12)
toasting forks for everyone (or a green stick)

How to cook:
Place a marshmallow on toasting fork. Hold over coals, turning slowly, don't let it melt! Eat and enjoy.

Answers to Puzzles

Don't look at these until you've tried the puzzles on page 34.

Farmer puzzles

Puzzle No 1

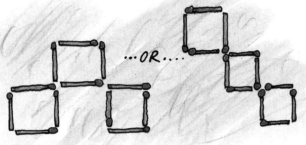

...OR....

Puzzle No 2

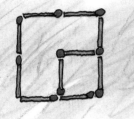

Perfect match

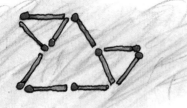

Triangle tricks

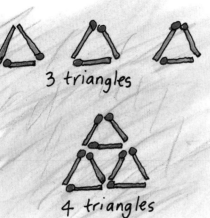

3 triangles

4 triangles

Grid puzzle

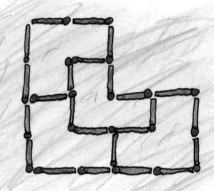

A difficult one

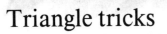

A trick one

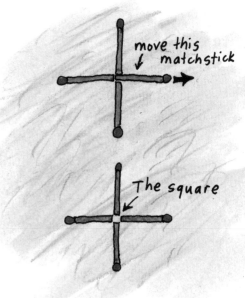

move this matchstick

The square

48